With very grateful thanks to Mike Seabrook, Morse Modaberi, Sonya Newland, Helen Johnson and Helen Courtney.

First published in Great Britain by Brockhampton Press, 20 Bloomsbury Street, London WC1B 3QA. A member of the Hodder Headline Group.

ISBN 1 86019 820 1

A copy of the C.I.P. data is available from the British Library upon request.

Created and produced by Flame Tree Publishing, a part of The Foundry Creative Media Company Limited, The Long House, Antrobus Road, Chiswick, London W4 5HY.

The Mind Bending Riddle Book

by Mike Seabrook

With illustrations by Morse Modaberi

BROCKHAMPTON PRESS

Introduction

The riddle is one of the most ancient forms of human play, certainly among the oldest forms of word play. It is also a substantially grey area, overlapping the territory of logic problems, for example: most riddles, even the simplest children's riddle-me-ree kind involve some degree of logical elimination. At the other end of the spectrum, a good many horrendously sophisticated and complicated problems could legitimately be called riddles. In between, the riddle embraces a great variety of quips, question-and-answer routines and, in general, a great many of the kind of games and verbal conundrums beloved of children for centuries.

In this little book we have deliberately erred on the side of generosity, in our interpretation of what is and is not a riddle. There are plenty of orthodox puzzles, ancient and modern, many of them for children, as well as a collection of more complicated, logic-problem-style riddles which have been added to tease the brain and provide a new outlook on riddle-solving.

Questions

Q. 1: **A frog is seated on a lily pad in the centre of a circular ornamental pond, sixteen feet in radius. When he wants to go ashore, he begins by jumping exactly eight feet onto another lily pad. From then onwards he always jumps exactly half the distance left between him and the edge. How many jumps will he take to get ashore?**

Q. 2: An entertainer performed her act to music. One day the conductor was unwell and his replacement took the music a little faster than the regular man. He was directly responsible for the entertainer's death. Why?

Q. 3: Who introduced the walking stick?

Q. 4: **Three men are found dead at a party. At the inquests it is established that in two cases the cause of death was a pin, and the third man died from a punch. But one of the two whose cause of death was a pin bore no signs of puncture: indeed, the only sign of damage on his body was a bruise on the back of his head; and the other two bore no signs of violence at all. What had happened?**

Q. 5: **What gets wetter as it dries?**

Q. 6: **A hungry bookworm decides to have an encyclopedia for lunch. The volumes are side by side in unbroken sequence along the shelf, volume one at the left-hand end. Each volume is two inches thick, and each cover is one eighth of an inch. The bookworm eats both paper and cover board at the same rate, half an inch per hour. If he starts at the first page of volume one, how long will it take him to eat his way to the last page of volume five?**

Q. 7: It stands on one leg with its heart in its head. What is it?

Q. 8: Write one hundred and add one,
And then with five unite;
When one and fifty you have joined,
You'll have what is polite.

Q. 9: My first of anything is half,
My second is complete;
And so remains until once more
My first and second meet.
What am I?

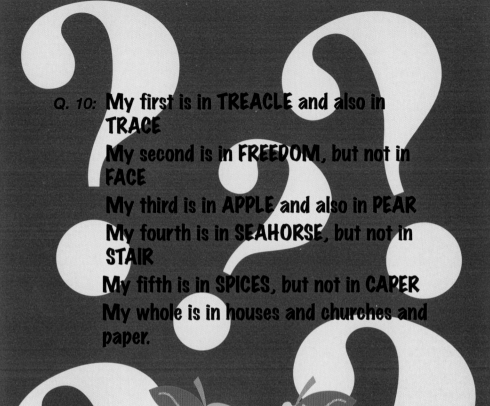

Q. 10: My first is in **TREACLE** and also in **TRACE**

My second is in **FREEDOM**, but not in **FACE**

My third is in **APPLE** and also in **PEAR**

My fourth is in **SEAHORSE**, but not in **STAIR**

My fifth is in **SPICES**, but not in **CAPER**

My whole is in houses and churches and paper.

Q. 11: If a ton of coal costs £125 and a ton of coke costs £90, what will half a ton of each come to?

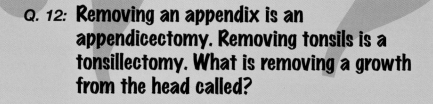

Q. 12: Removing an appendix is an appendicectomy. Removing tonsils is a tonsillectomy. What is removing a growth from the head called?

Q. 13: I have a mouth, I do not speak;
I have four eyes, but cannot see;
I have a bed, but do not sleep;
Can you tell me who I be?

The following riddle is thought to have been invented by Lewis Carroll, who was fascinated by all kinds of problem and conundrum:

I have a large box, with two lids, two caps, three established measures, and a great number of articles a carpenter cannot do without. Then I have always by me a couple of good fish, and a number of a smaller tribe, besides two lofty trees, fine flowers and the fruit of an indigenous plant; a handsome stag; two playful animals; and a number of a smaller and less tame herd; also two halls, or places of worship; some weapons of war and many weathercocks; the steps of a hotel; the House of Commons on the eve of a dissolution; two students or scholars, and some Spanish Grandees, to wait upon me. All pronounce me a wonderful piece of mechanism, but few have numbered up the strange medley of things which compose my whole.

What is he describing?

Q. 15: **A very ancient riddle:
As I was going to St Ives,
I met a man with seven wives.
Every wife had seven sacks,
Every sack had seven cats,
Every cat had seven kits;
Kits, cats, sacks and wives,
How many were going to St Ives?**

Q. 16: If you saw a swan with two nicks in its bill swimming in the upper reaches of the River Thames, where would it have come from?

Q. 17: What four things you can eat can you never have for breakfast?

Q. 18: What would you call a man who did not have all his fingers on his right hand?

Q. 19: **Lewis Carroll's first riddle:**
A monument – men all agree –
Am I in all sincerity,
Half cat, half hindrance made.
If head and tail removed should be,
Then most of all you strengthen me;
Replace my head, the stand you see
On which my tail is laid.

Q. 20: What has six legs, two heads, four ears and two hands, and walks on four feet?

Q. 21: A father and son were hurt in an accident. The father died in the ambulance on the way to hospital. The son was rushed in for emergency surgery. The surgeon, on seeing him, immediately refused to operate, saying, 'I can't work on him, he's my son.' How?

Q. 22: If two birds can lay up to eight eggs in two days, how many eggs can one peacock lay in three days?

Q. 23: When is a coat ineffective against the cold?

Q. 24: In a ravine in the desert a man is found dead. At the narrowest point of the ravine a pole has been slung from one cliff to the other, and the man has been hanged from a noose from this pole. Thirty feet below his feet is the lorry he had been driving through the desert. There is one set of clear footprints, from the cab of the lorry to the tailgate, which indicates that nothing has happened to obliterate any clues: there cannot have been any other tracks, because if they had been blown away by the wind or whatever, so would the one set that is found. Yet there is no clue to how he got from the lorry in the bottom of the ravine to the top to put the pole between the two sides, sling his noose from it and himself from the noose.

The coroner brings in a verdict that the man hanged himself, and everyone knows for certain that the verdict is correct. How do they know, and how did he do it?

Q. 25: Two fathers and two sons went shooting, and each shot one pheasant. How come only three pheasants went into the pot that night?

Q. 26: A plane crashes right on the border between Fascist Ruritania and Communist Bolonia, who have no diplomatic relations and are always in a state of near-war. The wreckage is strewn on both sides of the border. On which side of the border will the survivors be buried?

Q. 27: A farmer raises wheat in the dry season, and pigs and dairy cattle all the year round. What does he raise in the rainy season?

Q. 28: My first is in RADAR and also in DRIVEN
My second is in OBVIOUS and also in OAK
My third is in LION and also in LIMIT
My fourth is in PEANUT and also in PILE
My fifth is in HAPPINESS, but never in SAD
My sixth is in INVERNESS and also in INDIA
My seventh is in NIGHT and also in OCEAN
My whole is in seas and rivers and world.

Q. 29: What's the proper way to get down from a camel?

Q. 30: How many cubic yards of earth are there in a hole eight feet long by six wide and three deep?

Q. 31: A neat riddle coined by Lord Chesterfield in his celebrated letters to his son:
Scorned by the meek and humble mind,
And often by the vain possessed,
Heard by the deaf, seen by the blind.
I give the troubled spirit rest.

Q. 32: **I have a barrel without any beer.**
My sight is advanced, but I have no eyes.
I have many chambers, but none are my home.
What am I?

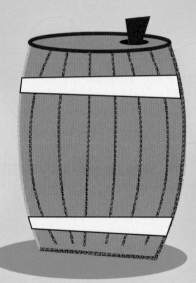

Q. 33: My first is in DELIGHT and also in DREAM

My second is in ASQUITH, but not in QUEEN

My third is in YESTERDAY and also in TODAY

My fourth is in APRIL, but never in MAY

My fifth is in ITCHING and also in SIGHT

My sixth is in GRACEFUL and also in FLIGHT

My seventh is in HEAVEN and also in HELL

My eighth is in TALKING and also in TELL

My whole is in mornings, long evenings and fun

Covering all with the warmth of the sun.

Q. 34: What has got eight wheels and flies?

Q. 35: Jack is asked how old he is. His reply is: 'The day before yesterday I was fifteen. Next year I shall be eighteen.' What does this mean, and what date was his birthday?

Q. 36: Lewis Carroll again:

A Russian had three sons. The first, named Rab, became a lawyer; the second, Yrma, became a soldier. The third became a sailor, what was his name?

Q. 37: What can go up a chimney down, but cannot go down a chimney up?

Q. 38: He who makes it, makes it to sell,
He who buys it does not use it,
He who uses it does not know it.
What is it?

Q. 39: Make three-quarters of a cross
And a circle complete;
Let two semi-circles
On a perpendicular meet;
Next add a triangle
That stands on two feet;
Next two semi-circles,
And a circle complete.
What am I?

Q. 40: **My second is performed by my first; and, it is thought, a thief by the marks of my whole might be caught. What am I?**

Q. 41: **A man died in 1997, and was buried in 1996. He was dead before his body was interred. What happened?**

Q. 42: How can you tell if you were built upside down?

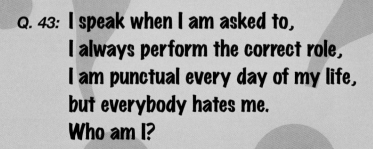

Q. 43: I speak when I am asked to,
I always perform the correct role,
I am punctual every day of my life,
but everybody hates me.
Who am I?

Q. 44: **What walks all day on its head?**

Q. 45: **The following is the famous riddle asked by the Sphinx to Oedipus in Sophocles' play of the same name:**
What goes by four legs at dawn, two legs at midday and three legs in the evening?

Q. 46: **What is the difference between a bird with one wing and a bird with two wings?**

Cuckoo
Cuckoo

Q. 47: **What is the following description of:**
There was a little green house;
In the little green house was a little brown house;
In the little brown house was a little yellow house;
In the little yellow house was a little white house;
In the little white house was a little white heart?

Q. 48: **What is lower with a head than without one?**

Q. 49: **Make sense of this sentence: 'It was and I said not all.'**

Q. 50: **A woman driving alone stopped at a filling station for petrol. From the moment she pulled out onto the road again she noticed a man in a car following her and flashing his lights. She tried everything she knew to shake him off: accelerating, slowing down, making sudden turns into side roads and so forth, but he stayed close on her tail. In the end she pulled into a police station and was amazed to see him follow her in. He was a complete stranger to her, he was not a policeman and there was nothing wrong with her car. Why did he follow her?**

Q. 51: Three-fourths of a lion, one half of an ass, which is the city that's covered with brass?

Q. 52: The following riddle was written by the Irish novelist James Joyce:
Brother and sister had he none,
Yet that man's father was his grandfather's son.

Q. 53: What grows bigger the more you take away?

Q. 54: **I have no head but I wear a cap. I have no feet but I stand up straight. What am I?**

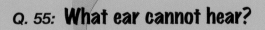

Q. 55: **What ear cannot hear?**

I was told that the following riddle was used by the FBI in their training of new agents in interrogation technique. Apparently the examinee was told it, then had to elicit the full story by question-and-answer, being allowed to ask only questions to which the examiner was able to reply 'yes' or 'no'. Whether it's true or not, it's certainly fun to try it on people, so here it is.

Eight men are gathered together in a remote desert. They are waiting for something. After a time the drone of a plane is heard. It approaches, and eventually a light aircraft comes into view. It circles the eight men, banks, comes down closer. A door opens in the side of the plane, a package is thrown out, and the plane flies off into the distance and disappears. The eight men run to the package and examine it. It turns out to be a human arm, neatly wrapped in surgical dressings and outer packaging. They look at it, look at one another, nod their satisfaction; then they bury the arm in the desert sand, and go their separate ways – as far as we know, not to meet again.

In a very exclusive club bar in New York two men meet. One of them is an eminent surgeon, the other nobody in particular. The surgeon presents the other with a banker's cheque for half a million dollars. The other man examines it, expresses his satisfaction, and they part.

Q. 57: My first is in MAYBE and also in MIGHT
My second is in STRONG, but not in SIGHT
My third is in NASTY and also in NIGHTMARE
My fourth is in SELFISH and also AWARE
My fifth is in CITY, but not in HOVEL
My whole is in banks and writers of novels.

Q. 58: **A man goes to market and buys a duck, a pet fox and a bag of grain. He comes to a river which can only be crossed by a rowing boat which he can use to ferry himself and his purchases across. It is only big enough to take the man and one of his items at once. He cannot leave the fox unattended with the duck, and he cannot leave the duck with the grain. How does he do it?**

Q. 59: **Another man came to the same river with the same three purchases, but HIS fox ate grain as well as ducks, so he could not leave the fox with either the duck or the grain, or either fox or duck with the grain. How did he do it?**

GRAIN

Q. 60: **A man is found lying dead in the middle of a field with an unopened package beside him. There are no tracks, no one is anywhere to be seen, he has not been shot, stabbed or in any other obvious way attacked. How did he die?**

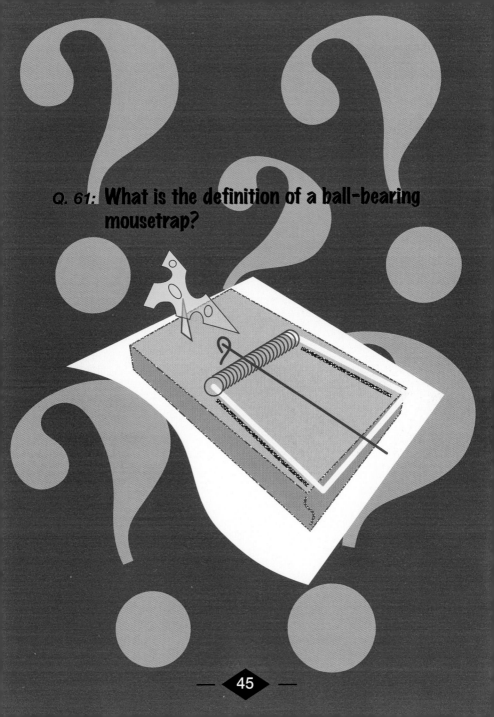

Q. 61: **What is the definition of a ball-bearing mousetrap?**

Q. 62: **Two bodies have I, though both joined in one. The more still I stand, the quicker I run. What am I?**

Q. 63: **What does a bat do in winter?**

Q. 64: **Why do Chinese men eat more rice than Japanese men?**

Q. 65: A traveller in a remote land comes to a fork in the road. He knows nothing of what lies ahead, except one thing: the road to the left leads to certain death, the one to the right to safety.

Beside the road are two local natives. One belongs to a tribe who never tell the truth, the other to a rival tribe who never tell lies. Unfortunately they look alike and there is no way he can tell which belongs to the truthful tribe and which to the lying tribe.

The traveller may ask either native for help, but he may ask only ONE question in all. What question can he ask which will enable him to take the correct road, whichever native he asks, and whatever answer the native gives?

Q. 66: I am a word of five letters. Take away two and only one will be left. What is the word?

Q. 67: With thieves I consort,
With the vilest, in short,
I'm quite at my ease in depravity;
Yet all divines use me,
And savants can't lose me,
For I am the centre of gravity.

Q. 68: **How could you be seriously injured by being hit with tomatoes?**

Q. 69: **My first is in FUTURE and also TODAY**
My second is in ORANGE, but never in PLAY
My third is in MIDNIGHT, but not at NOON
My fourth is in OPERA, but not in TUNE
My fifth is in REGULAR and also in RELAY
My sixth, like above is RELIABLE, not FEY
My seventh is OFT seen in OBVIOUS places
My eighth is in WINDOWS, but not in SPACES.
My whole is in time, be it tiresome or keen
After today I will always be seen.

Q. 70: **When is a rook not a bird?**

Q. 71: **When is sweetcorn the same as a swan?**

Q. 72: A man is wanted for a murder. The police have been given a tip-off that he will be at a certain address. They raid the place, and find a plumber, two lorry-drivers, a bricklayer and a bank manager playing cards. They have no description of the man they want, but they unhesitatingly arrest the plumber, who promptly confesses. How did they know to arrest him?

Q. 73: I have a nose that cannot smell,
I have two eyes but cannot see.
I have a head, a chest, a neck,
but none are any use to me.
I cannot walk, I cannot run
I can't abide to see the sun.
My day of birth is the eve of my life.
Who am I?

Q. 74: **What process must one use to transform a book into water?**

Q. 75: **A man was killed by a single blow to the head with a blunt instrument. The CID were summoned by the murderer. When they arrived they saw the murder weapon, and when they left they took it away with them. They ate a meal with the murderer, but they did not solve the case. What happened?**

Q. 76: **Although in number I'm the smallest,**
O'er kings I reign, and beat the tallest.
What am I?

Answers

A. 1: He will never reach dry land: there will always be half the distance to cross.

A. 2: The entertainer was a tightrope walker whose act was to walk the high wire blindfold. Her cue to step off the wire onto the platform, 100 feet up, was when the music stopped. The replacement conductor was unaware of the vital importance of the timing of the piece, finished seconds early, and she stepped off the wire into thin air.

A. 3: Eve – when she presented Adam with a little Cain.

A. 4: The man dead from a punch had drunk himself to death on the potent punch served at the party. The first man dead from a pin had tried to drink dry a small barrel of beer brought by one of the revellers, and had died of alcoholic poisoning before he made it. The barrel was a pin, which is a small cask or barrel holding nine gallons. The other dead man had fallen asleep in a drunken stupor on the floor in a quiet corner, right beneath the trestles on which the pin was standing. At some point it fell off its chocks and landed on the back of his head, killing him instantly.

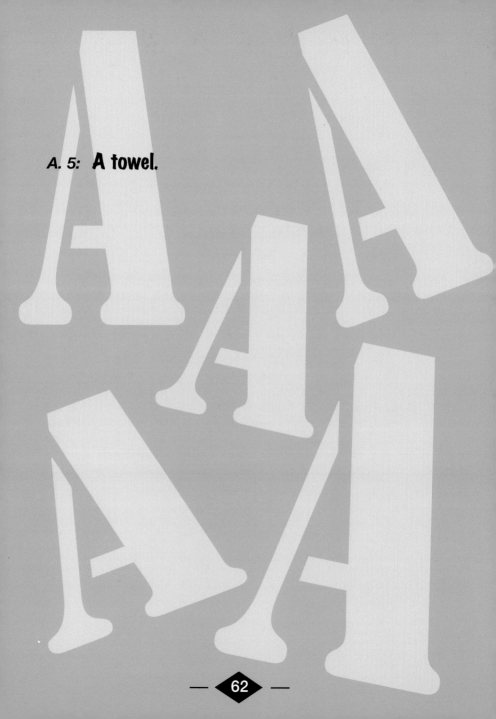

A. 5: **A towel.**

A. 6: Starting from page one he will eat through the front cover, coming next to the back cover of volume one. When he gets to the last page of volume five it will be just before the back cover. He will thus have to eat through five 2-inch volumes and eight covers of one eighth each, making a further inch. Eleven inches at half an inch per hour = 22 hours.

A. 7: A cabbage.

A. 8: **CIVIL (Roman numerals).**

A. 9: **A semicircle.**

A. 10: **TREES.**

A. 11: **Ashes.**

A. 12: **A haircut.**

A. 13: **The Mississippi River.**

A. 14: **Here is the answer:**
The WHOLE is MAN.
The PARTS are as follows:
A large box – the chest.
Two lids – the eyelids.
Two caps – the kneecaps.
Three established measures – the nails, hands and feet.
A great number of articles a carpenter cannot do without – nails.
A couple of good fish – the soles of the feet.
A number of a smaller tribe – the muscles (mussels).
Two lofty trees – the palms (of the hands).
Fine flowers – two lips (tulips), and irises.
The fruit of an indigenous plant – hips.

A handsome stag – the heart (hart).

Two playful animals – the calves.

A number of a smaller and less tame herd – the hairs (hares).

Two halls, or places of worship – the temples.

Some weapons of warfare – the arms and shoulder blades.

Many weathercocks – the veins (vanes).

The steps of an hotel – the insteps (inn-steps).

The House of Commons on the eve of a dissolution – the eyes and nose (ayes and noes).

Two students or scholars – the pupils of the eye.

Some Spanish Grandees – the tendons (ten dons).

A. 15: **1 man plus 7 wives plus 49 sacks plus 343 cats plus 2401 kits makes 2801. Plus the narrator makes 2802. Was the group bound for St Ives or going the other way? And of course in the broader sense we have no idea how many were going to St Ives. But 2802 would get my vote, since it's obvious enough that that's what the rhymester meant. Isn't it?**

A. 16: **An egg.**

A. 17: **Lunch, dinner, supper and tea.**

A. 18: **Normal. Most of us prefer to have some on the left hand as well.**

A. 19: **A tablet.**

A. 20: **A horse – with its rider.**

A. 21: **The surgeon was the boy's mother.**

A. 22: **None. Peacocks don't lay eggs.**

A. 23: **When it is a coat of arms.**

A. 24: He used the cargo from his lorry, stacking it up and climbing up it with the pole and rope, which he had in the lorry with him. After he had slung the pole, tied the noose and hanged himself, the cargo disappeared in the desert sun: the lorry was refrigerated, and the cargo was blocks of ice.

A. 25: The men who went were a grandfather, his son and the son's son, his grandson.

A. 26: **Neither: even Fascist and Communist countries do not make a habit of burying survivors.**

A. 27: **His umbrella.**

A. 28: **DOLPHIN.**

A. 29: **You cannot get down from a camel. Try a duck.**

A. 30: **None: there's no earth in a hole.**

A. 31: **Nothing.**

A. 32: **A gun.**

A. 33: **DAYLIGHT.**

A. 34: Two corporation dustcarts.

A. 35: When he is asked and gives this enigmatic reply, it is January 1, and Jack is 16 years and one day old. The day before yesterday, when he was 15, was December 30. His 16th birthday was on December 31. He will therefore be 17 this coming December 31, and will therefore be 18 during the course of next year.

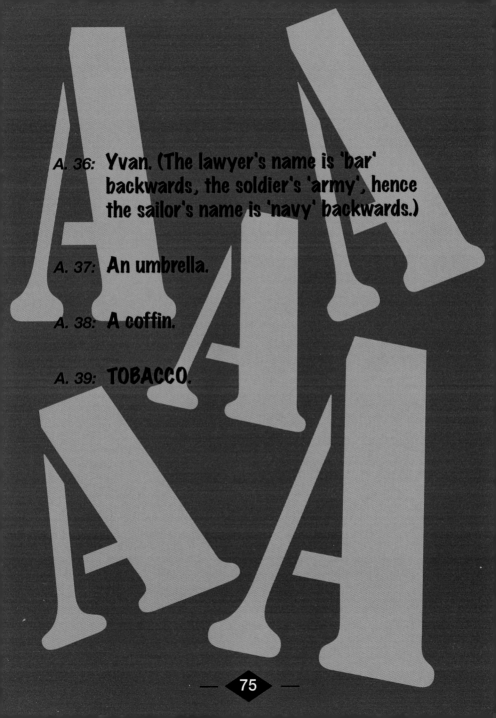

A. 36: **Yvan. (The lawyer's name is 'bar' backwards, the soldier's 'army', hence the sailor's name is 'navy' backwards.)**

A. 37: **An umbrella.**

A. 38: **A coffin.**

A. 39: **TOBACCO.**

A. 40: **A footstep.**

A. 41: **He died on 1 January, but had left instructions that he was to be buried in the village of his birth, a few miles away. The village was on the other side of the International Date Line, so when his corpse was taken there it became yesterday, so to speak, which is how he came to be buried on 31 December of the previous year.**

A. 42: **If your nose runs and your feet smell.**

A. 43: **An alarm clock.**

A. 44: **A nail in a horseshoe.**

A. 45: **A man – a baby crawls, an adult walks on two legs and a elderly man walks with a stick.**

A. 46: **It's a matter of a pinion.**

A. 47: **A walnut.**

A. 48: **A pillow.**

A. 49: **All it requires is punctuation: It was 'and' I said, not 'all'.**

A. 50: **While she was away from her car paying for the petrol, another man had slipped into the back of her car and hidden behind the front seats. The man in the car behind saw what happened and followed the woman to warn her – flashing his lights so the attacker would know he was being watched. The man in the car behind was hoping to warn her or to intervene if she was attacked. He was relieved to see her go to the police station.**

A. 51: **London.**

A. 52: **A man regarding himself in the glass.**

A. 53: **A hole.**

A. 54: **A mushroom.**

A. 55: **An ear of corn.**

A. 56: **What you have to elicit by questioning is the rest of the story. The eight men in the desert and the surgeon were once members of the same army unit, whose plane was forced down in a desert region during wartime. They were forced to trek hundreds of miles to find civilization, and after a time their rations were finished and they were beginning to starve. Eventually, faced with death, they agreed to donate one arm each to feed the lot of them. They drew lots to determine the order in which they should sacrifice their limbs, the understanding being that the surgeon should operate to amputate the arms and, therefore, that he should be the last to give up an arm. As time went on, eight donated arms, but just as the surgeon was about to help them in the amputation of his own arm, they were rescued.**

After the war they went their separate ways, but first made a pact that the surgeon would honour his agreement and send the others a sign to meet and receive his arm. What he actually did was to disappear, resurfacing in New York, where he built up a practice, becoming fabulously rich in the process. Eventually he found a derelict, offered him a million dollars to let him amputate one arm. The down-and-out agreed, went to stay at the surgeon's expensive clinic on Long Island, gave up an arm, and received half his promised fee. When the surgeon received a coded message that his sacrifice had been examined and found satisfactory, he met the derelict one more time, to pay the remainder of the fee, and that was the end of the story.

A. 57: **MONEY.**

A. 58: He takes the duck to the far side,
returns, and takes the fox over. Leaving
the fox on the far side he takes the duck
back with him, leaves it on the near side
and takes the grain over. Leaving this
with the fox, he returns empty and
finally takes the duck. But...

A. 59: **He ferried the fox over first, returned and took the grain. On both return trips he had the duck tethered to the boat, and it swam beside him!**

A. 60: **The unopened package is a parachute, which failed to open.**

A. 61: A tom cat.

A. 62: An hourglass.

A. 63: It splits if you don't oil it.

A. 64: There are a lot more men in China than there are in Japan.

A. 65: If he chances to choose the truthful native, there is no problem. He will get a truthful answer either way. It is to guard against his picking the lying native that he must formulate his question carefully.

What he must do is to indicate one of the roads – it doesn't matter which – and ask either native: 'If I asked you if that road led to safety, would you say 'Yes'?'

If the road he picks does lead to safety, the lying native, if asked the direct question, would answer NO. Thus, asked if he would say YES, the truthful answer would be NO, I WOULDN'T. But since he always lies, he is forced to answer YES. If, on the other hand, the road the traveller indicates does NOT lead to safety, the direct question would bring a reply of YES from the liar. Asked the oblique question, he is once again forced to reply NO. Thus the traveller knows that if his native happens to be the liar, he can still be sure that if the reply is YES the road he has indicated leads to safety, and if it is NO, it leads to danger.

A. 66: **STONE.**

A. 67: **The letter V.**

A. 68: **If they were tinned tomatoes.**

A. 69: **TOMORROW.**

A. 70: **When it is part of a chess set.**

A. 71: **When it is a cob.**

A. 72: **The lorry-drivers, the bricklayer and the bank manager were all women.**

A. 73: **A snowman.**

A. 74: **Add an 'r' (Brook).**

A. 75: The man was killed by his mother, who clubbed him to death with a frozen chicken. Then she put it in the oven and it was nicely roasted when she summoned the police. They accepted her invitation to stay and eat with her, thus disposing of the murder weapon.

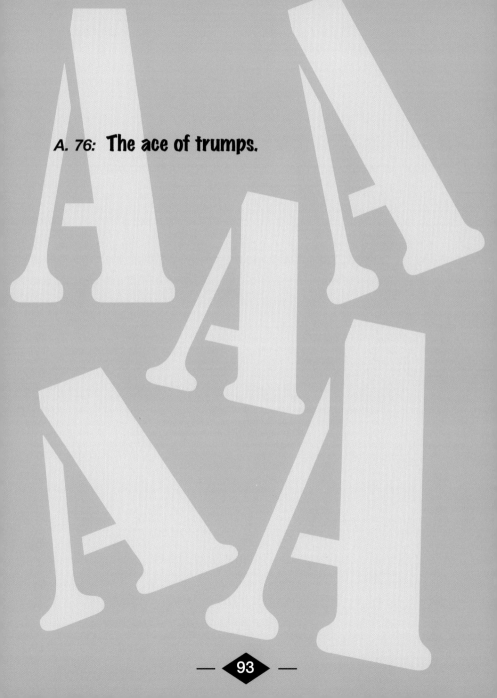

A. 76: **The ace of trumps.**